POCKET PUZZLES

Published and distributed by
TOBAR LIMITED
The Old Aerodrome, Worlingham, Beccles,
Suffolk, NR34 7SP, UK

www.tobar.co.uk

This edition printed 2010

Printed in China

ISBN: 978-1-903230-13-8

Contents

Matchstick Puzzles

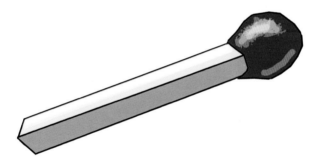

Puzzle 1

Rearrange three of these six matches to produce four equilateral triangles

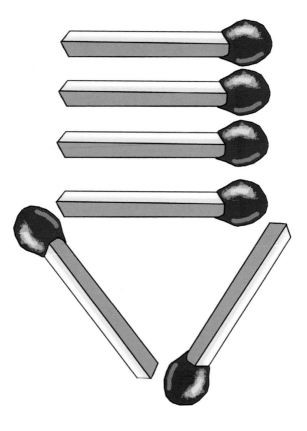

Puzzle 2

In this puzzle there are nine matches that make up three equilateral triangles. Move three matches and make four equilateral triangles.

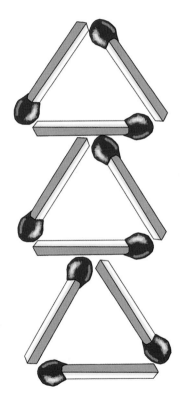

Puzzle 3

Here we have a button trapped inside a tuning fork. Move any two matches to get the button outside the tuning fork, but keep the exact shape of the tuning fork.

Hint

The tuning fork can end up facing in any direction!

Puzzle 4

Move six of the matches in the diagram to leave two.

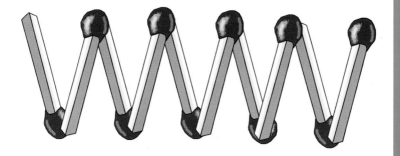

Hint

This is a wordy puzzle!

Puzzle 5

Is it possible to turn these three matches into six without splitting or breaking them?

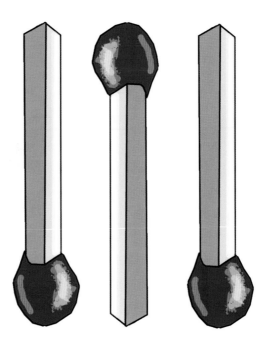

Hint

The Romans knew how to do this!

Puzzle 6

This puzzle shows five squares. Can you move
three matches to make four squares?
Every match must be part of a completed square,
you are not allowed any 'loose ends' in this puzzle.
You cannot take any matches away
or stack matches on top of each other!

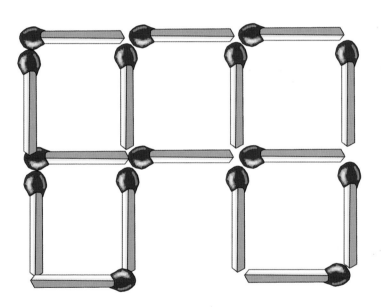

Puzzle 7

This rocket is heading towards you at a great speed! Quickly, move just three matches and the cockpit button, to send it rocketing skywards again!

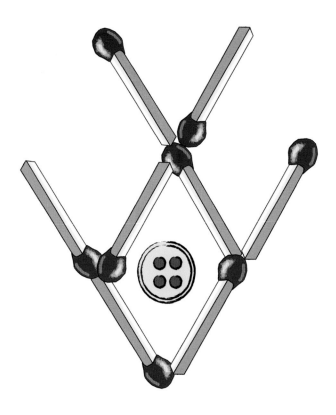

Puzzle 8

Build a tic-tac-toe grid like this one, from twelve matchsticks. Now, moving only four matchsticks, create three squares and a triangle.

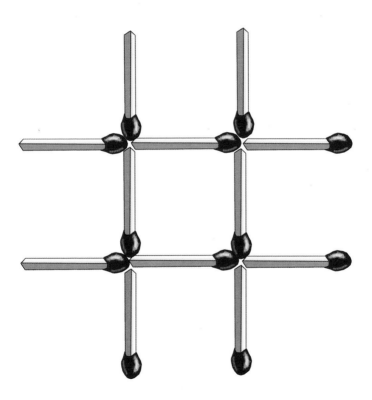

Puzzle 9

Move two matchsticks to create a shape
with five squares in it.

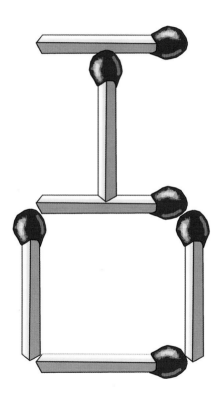

Puzzle 10

Using 40 matchsticks, create a shape like this – with
16 squares. Now, remove nine matchsticks to leave
a shape that has no squares in it at all.
You should end up with seven larger rectangles,
but no squares!

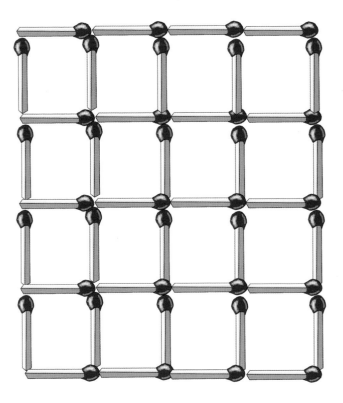

Puzzle 11

In this shape there are three triangles. Move three matches to produce a new shape that contains five triangles.

Puzzle 12

Move two matches to make these
six matches into nothing.

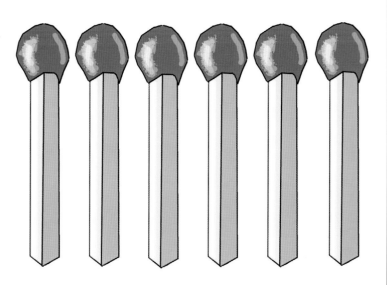

Puzzle 13

Add eight matches to this L shape to create four smaller L shapes enclosed within the original one.

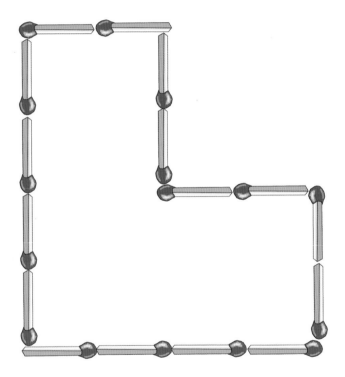

Puzzle 14

Look very carefully at this diagram. Now move one match to make a square.

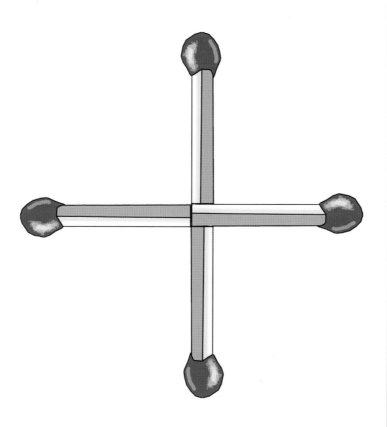

Puzzle 15

This shape contains four squares, each the same size. Now, move four matches to create a shape with three squares in it, again all of the same size.

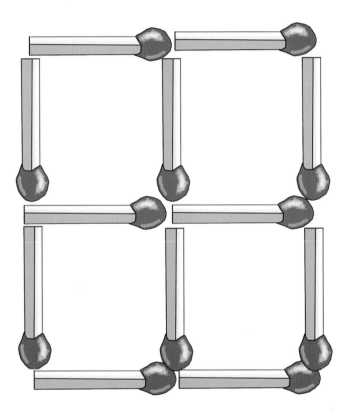

Puzzle 16

This is a classic among match puzzles, and has been
around for many years in various forms.
It may even be over 100 years old!
You have to change the two wine glasses into
a house by moving six matches.

Puzzle 17

This shape is made up of nine small squares.
Take away eight matches to leave five small squares.

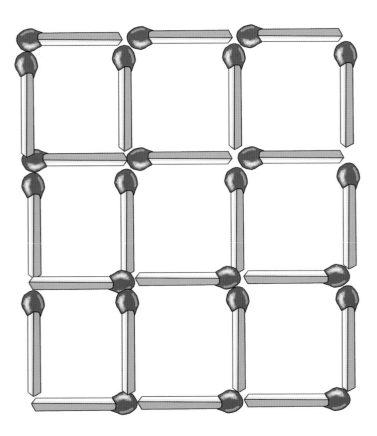

Puzzle 18

This shape is made up of three triangles in a line.
Move two matches to create a shape made
up of four triangles in the same line.

Puzzle 19

Arrange these five matches so that every single
match is touching every other match.

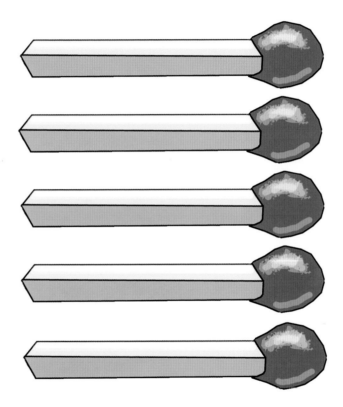

Puzzle 20

Move two matches to create a clock face
showing the time at twenty to four.

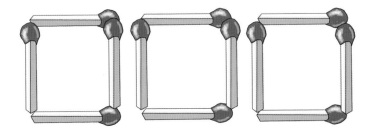

Puzzle 21

Using just three matchsticks, see if you can create fourteen capital letters of the alphabet.

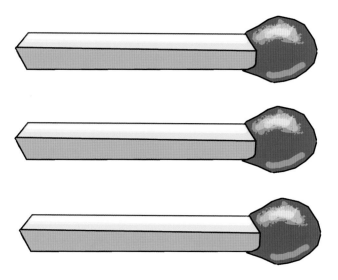

Coin
Puzzles

Coin puzzle 1

In this layout of nine coins we can see there are eight ways that we can draw a straight line through rows of three coins. By moving two coins you should be able to find ten ways to draw a straight line through rows of three coins.

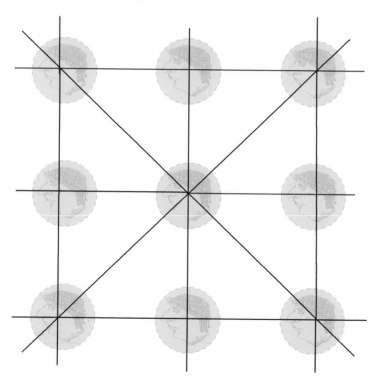

Coin puzzle 2

Arrange three gold coins and three silver coins as
shown in the diagram, and remember to leave
a coin width space in the middle –
shown by the yellow square.
You have to move all the gold coins to the right and
all the silver coins to the left. Gold coins can only
move to the right, and silver ones can only move left.
They are not allowed to go backwards.
You move a coin into an empty space by sliding it
into a vacant space, or by jumping over
another coin into an empty space.
It can be done in 15 moves.

Coin puzzle 3

Arrange six coins in two rows as shown in the top part of this diagram. Now, move three coins to produce the circle shape shown at the bottom. Each coin must touch at least two others at all times.

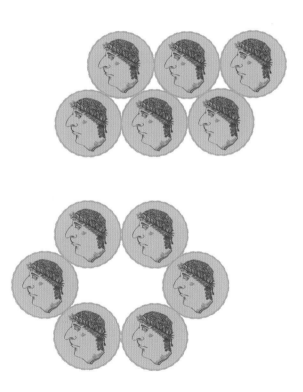

Coin puzzle 4

Turn this shape upside down by moving just two coins.

Coin puzzle 5

Lay out these four gold coins so that every coin
is touching every other coin.

Coin puzzle 6

In this puzzle we have a button trapped in a coin square of eight coins. Moving coins in touching pairs, make three moves to rebuild the square and free the button.

Coin puzzle 7

This square of eight coins has four rows of three coins. Add another coin to this diagram, but in such a way that there are still only four rows of three coins. The new coin must touch an existing coin, and should be placed in such a way that it becomes one of the four rows of three coins.

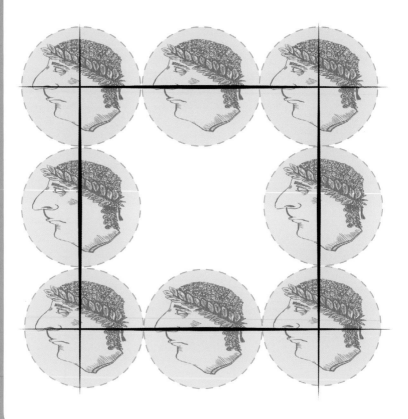

Coin puzzle 8

Move two coins to alter the direction of this arrow.

Coin puzzle 9

This L shape has two rows of three coins.
Add one more coin to give three rows of three coins.

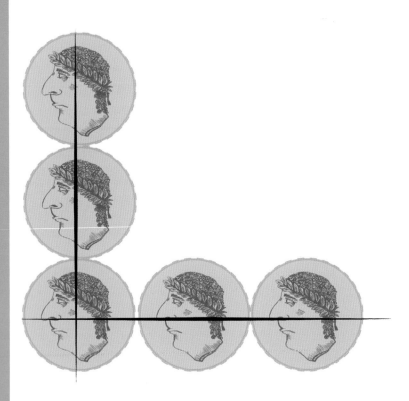

Coin puzzle 10

In this square of eight coins there are four rows of three coins. Place two new coins into this diagram to produce five rows of four coins.

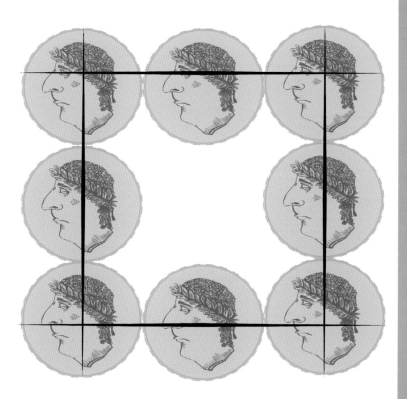

Coin puzzle 11

Add one more coin to this diagram so that all coins
can then be joined with five straight lines,
two of which must be diagonal. The lines must not
cross or touch each other.

Coin puzzle 12

Join these coins by drawing two straight lines.

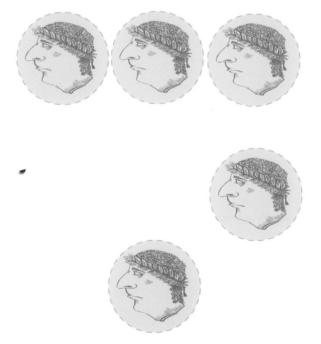

Coin puzzle 13

Here are eight coins laid out in a row.
Make four moves to end up with four stacks of
two coins. You jump a coin over any two other coins
and land on the next coin.

Coin puzzle 14

An eccentric diner left a gold sovereign as a tip, but only if the waiter could get it from under an upturned empty wine bottle without touching the bottle.
How did he do it?

Coin puzzle 15

You are playing chequers, badly, and have one bronze coin left. Your challenger takes pity on you, and says that you can keep every silver coin that you can jump over in one continuous play. It is possible to jump all ten silver coins in one go – how?

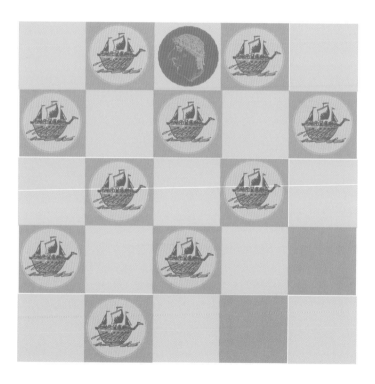

Coin puzzle 16

Turn this cube of nine coins into an arrow by moving four coins.

Coin puzzle 17

This coin square has four rows of three coins.
Move one coin to a new location and create
six rows of three coins.

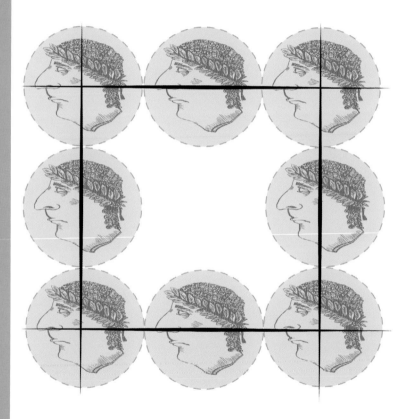

Coin puzzle 18

Move two coins to turn this triangle into a square.

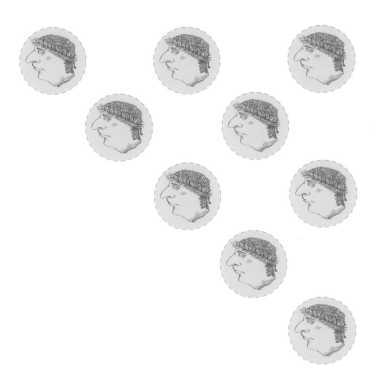

Coin puzzle 19

Build a pyramid from these ten coins.

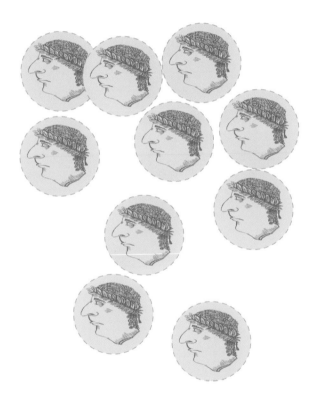

General Puzzles

General Puzzle 1

You will need a pocket handkerchief, rolled into a pipe shape, or a tie or a length of ribbon or string for this puzzle.
Place the handkerchief across the hand in the way shown in the diagram.
The puzzle – tie a knot using just one hand.

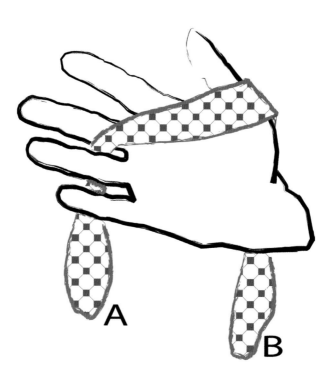

General puzzle 2

Take four £5 notes from your wallet or,
even better, someone else's!
Fold a 3mm border along the long edge of the notes,
and then fold the right hand vertical edge down
to meet the bottom edge, as shown in the illustration.
Using the four notes, recreate the shape of the notes,
but – of course – four times the size.

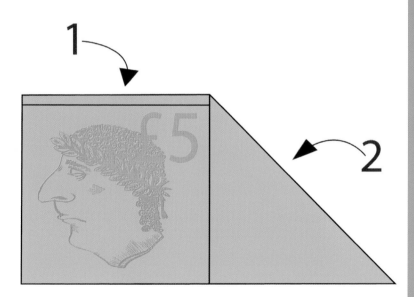

General puzzle 3

Take a banknote from your wallet or pocket and fold
loosely into an S shape as shown in the diagram.
Now, slide two paper clips on to the note as shown.
The puzzle is to remove the two paper clips from the
note without touching them, and for the two paper
clips to be joined together when they
come off the note.

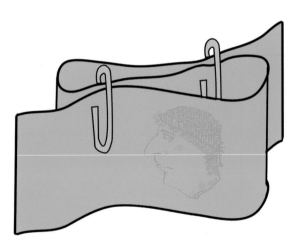

General puzzle 4

Take a pocket handkerchief, tie or hair ribbon and
grasp each end firmly with your hands.
Now, tie a knot without letting go with either hand.

Hint

*Think about the position of your hands and
arms before you pick it up!*

General puzzle 5

Take out four business cards, or gather them up from friends. Draw five spots on the back of each card, as shown. The puzzle is to place all four cards together in such a way that only four spots from each card are visible.

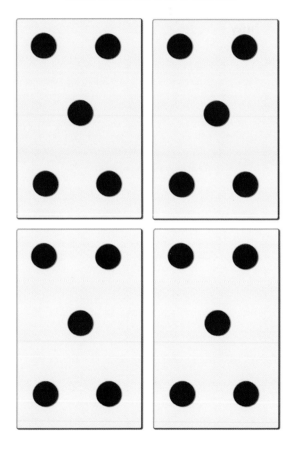

General puzzle 6

Take a business card, tube ticket or lottery ticket –
check first that you haven't won a million! Place a
round headed key on the ticket or card and draw
round it. Now, tear or cut a hole about 2 or 3 mm
smaller than the head of the key.
Check that the key cannot fit through the hole.
Now, how do you get the key to pass through
this hole without tearing the hole or
making the key smaller?

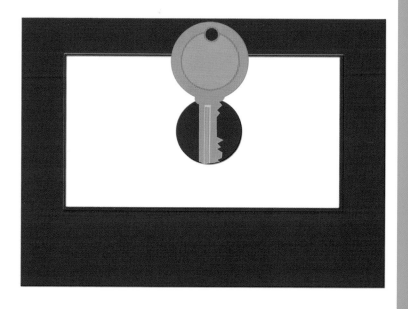

General puzzle 7

If you think that getting a key to drop through a business card is clever, why not try this next puzzle challenge. Take a business card, lottery ticket or post-card. Now, make a hole in the card big enough to fit your entire head through it!

You can rip or cut the card in any way that you think will help, but there is only one solution as far as I know.

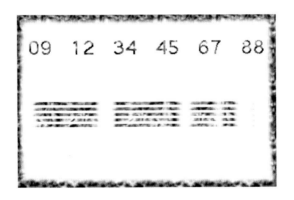

General puzzle 8

Draw two straight lines to connect these five key fob holes. The two lines must be straight, and they must meet at some point.

General puzzle 9

Take two brass keys and two steel keys. Place them
all in your left trouser pocket – the red shape
represents this. Now, move the four keys to your
right trouser pocket – represented by the blue shape.
There are, however, one or two 'rules' that
must be obeyed…
Keys moving from left to right must always
travel in pairs.
Keys moving from right to left can travel
in pairs or alone.
You cannot have keys made from different metals in
your right pocket until all the keys are
in the right pocket.

General puzzle 10

Lay out four keys as shown in the diagram.
You have to stack these keys, one on top of the other, so
that key number 2 is on the top of the stack, and key
number 4 is on the bottom.
Keys move by jumping over other keys to land on other
keys. They can only jump one gap at a time.
Key 2 is the only key that is allowed to jump into
a space, all other keys must land on top of existing keys.
The final key must be touching the stack, and simply
jumps on to the top.

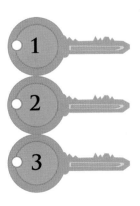

General puzzle 11

Arrange five keys so that four keys are touching every other key, and one key is touching at least three other keys.

General Puzzle 12

You have six sets of five chain links and you want to make a continuous chain. You do this by splitting a link and joining it to the next link.

What is the minimum number of links you need to split to make a continuous loop of chain?

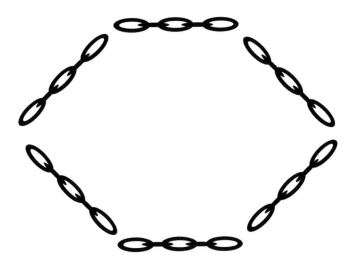

General Puzzle 13

Reverse the direction of this shape by moving the match plus 2 coins only.

Solutions

Solution 1

Make a pyramid with three of the matches and place this over the existing triangle as shown. This will give you four equilateral triangles

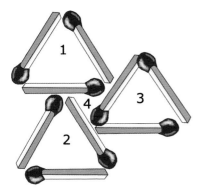

Solution 2

Move the three matches that form the top triangle down to the side of the bottom triangle. A small equilateral triangle (numbered 4 on the diagram) is created where the three triangles meet.

Solution 3

Slide the horizontal match along by half its length.
Next, pick up the top left match (shown as a faded image) and place it on the bottom right.
The tuning fork is now upside down, but the button is outside it.

Solution 4

Make a letter T with first two matches, and a letter O with the last four. You have moved six matches and spelled out the word TWO.

Solution 5

Make the first two matches into a V shape, and you then have VI, which is the number six in Roman numerals!

Solution 6

Move the left hand side match (seen as a faded image) up to make a vertical side at the top, and take the two matches from the top and right sides of the far right square to make the top and right hand sides of the new square.

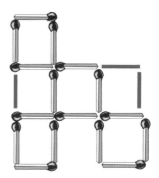

Solution 7

Move the three matches, shown in grey on the solution, to the other side of the puzzle. Now, move the cockpit button into the enclosed diamond space, and you have reversed the direction of the rocket!

Solution 8

Bring the two left hand sticks to a point – this creates your triangle. Now, take the furthest two sticks and use them to cap off the top and bottom of the grid – this creates your three squares. The grey shapes show where the sticks are taken from.

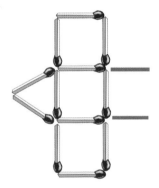

Solution 9

Place the two top matchsticks on top of the square shape in a cross formation. This will create four small squares to add to the existing one – total five squares!

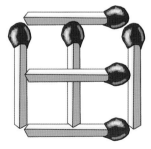

Solution 10

Using the diagram as a guide,
remove the nine missing matches
to give you the shape shown.

Solution 11

Move the left hand triangle to the top and
you have a shape with four small triangles,
and a large triangle around the outside of all
of them.

Solution 12

Angle the second match along to
make the letter N and rotate the
last match to make the bottom of
the letter L. This spells out the
word NIL.

Solution 13

Add the eight matches as shown in the diagram, and you have four smaller L shapes enclosed within the boundary of the original one.

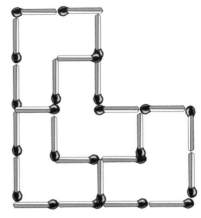

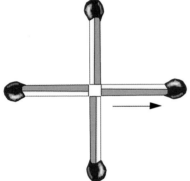

Solution 14

Slide the right hand match a little to the right, as shown in the diagram, and a small square will appear where the four matches join in the centre.

Solution 15

Take the two matches from the top left hand corner, and the two matches from the bottom right corner and create a new square to the right and above the original shape. You now have three squares.

Solution 16

Slide the two base matches together to form the floor of the house. Now, use the top left two matches and the top right two matches to make the shape shown.

Solution 17

Remove the four matches from the top right and the four from the bottom left and you will be left with this shape, which is made up of five small squares.

Solution 18

Move the two bottom left matches and place them over the spaces between the middle and right triangles and you have your four triangles!

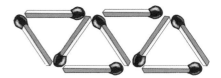

Solution 19

Lay the matches out in the shape shown, with a fan of two matches resting on top of a fan of three matches, and every match will be touching every other match somewhere.

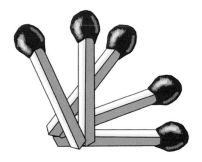

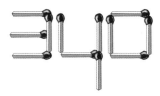

Solution 20

Move the left match of the first square to form a number three, and then take the top match from the centre square and drop it down to make the number three. The time shown is 3:40, or twenty to four. (I suppose I could have mentioned that it is a digital clock?!)

Solution 21

Here are the 14 we created – how did you do?

Coin solution 1

Move the two middle coins in to the gap between the centre coin and themselves, as shown in the diagram, and you can now see ten straight lines that pass through three coins.

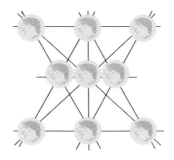

Coin solution 2

Number the coins as shown in this diagram, and move the coins in the following way…

Coin 5 to space 4
Coin 3 to space 5
Coin 2 to space 3
Coin 4 to space 2
Coin 6 to space 4
Coin 7 to space 6
Coin 5 to space 7
Coin 3 to space 5
Coin 1 to space 3
Coin 2 to space 1
Coin 4 to space 2
Coin 6 to space 4
Coin 5 to space 6
Coin 3 to space 5
Coin 4 to space 3

①　②　③　4　⑤　⑥　⑦

Coin solution 3

Number the coins as shown in the diagram.
1 Move coin 6 so that it touches coins 4 and 5
2 Move coin 5 so that it touches coins 2 and 3
3 Move coin 3 so that it touches coins 6 and 5

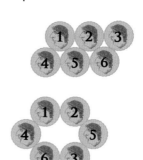

Coin solution 4

Move the two coins from the top left to the bottom right as shown by the arrows.

Coin solution 5

Lay three coins in a circle so that they are all touching, and then lay the fourth coin on top.

Coin solution 6

Number the eight coins as shown. Move coins 1 and 2 to the right of coin 3. Slide coins 7 and 8 along, so that 7 ends up at the bottom of the row of coins 3 and 5. Move coins 4 and 6 to fill the space below coin 2.
The button is now free and the square is rebuilt.

Coin solution 7

Add the coin to the top row as shown. The top row now has four coins instead of three, so it doesn't count as a row of three any more. You have also created a new, diagonal row of three coins. The result is a diagram, which still contains only four rows of three coins.

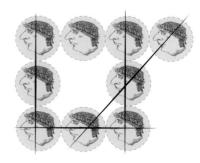

Coin solution 8

Take the two coins that form the tail, marked here with an X. Move these round to the bottom left, as shown, and the arrow is now pointing up and to the right.

Coin solution 9

Place a coin where shown, and you can now draw a new line of three coins.

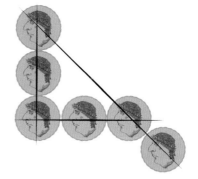

Coin solution 10

Place a coin on top of the two corners where shown, and you will have five rows of coins, each with four coins in it.

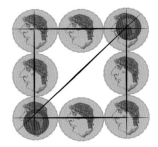

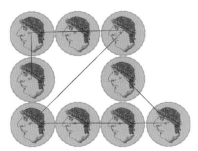

Coin solution 11

Arrange the coins as shown.

Coin solution 12

Draw a straight line from left to right through the top row of coins, and continue this line beyond the coins until you can bring it down diagonally to pass through the centres of the other two coins.

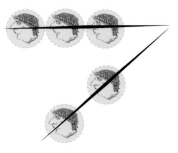

Coin puzzle 13

Here are eight coins laid out in a row. Make four moves to end up with four stacks of two coins. You jump a coin over any two other coins and land on the next coin.

Coin solution 14

The waiter took a blunt knife and smartly knocked the coin out from under the bottle. He did it so quickly that the coin slid out and the bottle dropped on to the table without falling over.

Coin solution 15

Jump the coins in the sequence shown and you get to keep all ten of them!

Coin solution 16

Move the four numbered coins to their new places and you have your arrow shape.

Coin solution 17

Move the right hand middle coin into the middle of the square and you now have two rows vertically, two rows horizontally and two rows diagonally. Total six!

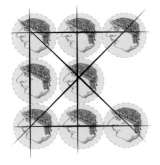

Coin solution 18

Pick up the two marked coins from the base of the triangle, and place them either side of the point. This creates your square.

Coin solution 19

Lay out a row of four coins.
Next, lay a row of three coins over
the joints of the first four coins.
Now, lay a row of two coins over
the joints of the three previous
coins, and top it off with a single
coin over the joint of the previous
two coins.

General solution 1

Keeping the end marked A trapped between
the 3rd and 4th fingers, reach down and
take hold of end B with the thumb and first
finger. Now, shake the hand downwards,
and the loop around the hand will drop over
your hand. Release end A – but keep a tight
grip on B, and you have tied a one-handed
knot!

General solution 2

I have used different colours in the
solution diagram to show how the four
notes fit together to make one large
shape.

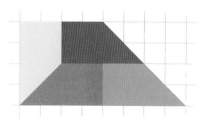

General solution 3

Take hold of the two ends of the banknote, as shown by the large red arrows, and pull them apart. The two paper clips will slide towards each other, then link with each other and jump off the note as you pull out the last curve.
Amazing!

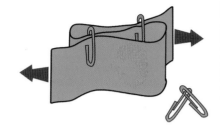

General solution 4

Cross your arms before you pick up the handkerchief and then slowly uncross them, keeping a tight grip of the handkerchief as you pull. The twist in your arms will be placed into the material, and when you have finished your arms will be unfolded and the cloth will be knotted.

General solution 5

Arrange the cards as shown in the solution diagram, with each card alternately overlapping and being overlapped by each other card. The result is four cards, each showing only four out of their five spots.

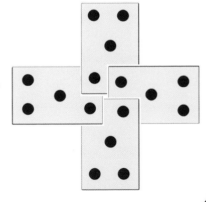

General solution 6

Fold the card in half and drop the key into the hole. It still won't fit through! However, if you gently push the corners of the card together – see the red arrows in the solution diagram, the card will fold along the dotted black line, and the hole will enlarge enough to allow the key to drop through.

When you open the card out flat again the hole is still the same size, and is undamaged.

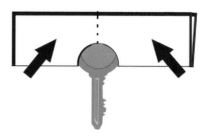

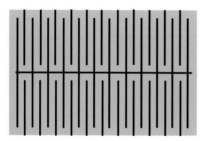

General solution 7

First cut a slit along the long edge of your card or ticket. Stop the slit about 5mm from the edge. Now, cut a series of slits in the way shown in the diagram.

Once all the slits are cut, open up the card – carefully – and you will find that it has become a large loop, through which you can easily put your head.

General solution 8

Draw a line through the top three holes and extend this line far enough so that you can draw a second line through the remaining key fob holes.

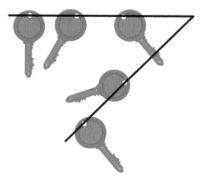

General solution 9

Move one brass and one steel key from left pocket to right pocket.
Move the steel key back to the left pocket.
Move one brass and one steel key from the left pocket to the right pocket.
Move the steel key back to the left pocket.
Move both steel keys from the left pocket to the right pocket.

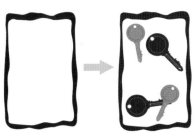

General solution 10

Key 1 jumps over key 2 and lands on key 3.
Key 2 jumps over stacked keys 1 and 2 and lands in the gap.
Key 1 jumps over key 2 and lands on key 4.
Key 3 jumps over key 2 and lands on stacked keys 4 and 1.
Key 2 is the last key, is touching the stack of keys 4, 1 and 3 and simply jumps up.
Key 4 is on the bottom of the stack and key 2 is on the top.

General solution 11

Lay one key down flat. Arrange three keys on top so that they are all touching each other and also the bottom key. Place the last key on top of the bottom key and press into the edge of the three keys

General Solution 12

If you split the chain at each gap in the diagram you will need to make six link joints. However, if you take one piece of five links and split them all open you can use these to join the other five pieces of chain. So the fewest number is five.

General Solution 13

Move the match from the bottom to the top of the diagram, and the bottom right and left coins to lie each side of the coin currently at the top.